Dear Parents

As we all know, from an early age, the information our children learn about religion will later influence their beliefs, attitudes, and behaviors in later years.

This series tells about the birth, infancy, and childhood of Prophet Muhammad (peace and blessings be upon him), with stories and drawings that will appeal to our children and help them to understand.

We hope and believe that you and your children will enjoy this series and find the stories not only entertaining, but informative as well.

THE HAPPY LAMBS

It was early morning; on the plateau where the Child of Light, the wonder of wonders, lived a sweet breeze had begun to blow. His scent was intermingled with the scent of the flowers. Halima's flock had started their day by taking deep breaths to inhale this lovely scent. Then they had started to graze. Their soft bleats combined with the beautiful ringing of the bells around their necks. The youngest lamb was smiling all over. He rubbed his face on the soft wool of his mother. His happiness beamed out at everyone.

4

In his highpitched voice he asked his mother: "Mommy, we are much luckier than all the other sheep, aren't we? I heard that the other sheep can't find enough food to eat, and that the mommy sheep don't have enough milk for their babies to drink. The drought has hit the other sheep and the people really hard, hasn't it?" The mother sheep looked on her lamb and lovingly answered him: "Yes, lambkins, what you say is true. We have to thank Allah very much for belonging to Halima. Everything started when Halima brought the Child of Light to her house. The Child of Light came to this plateau nearly four years ago."

5

6

The mother sheep continued; "From that day on Halima's house has been full of plenty and blessings."
"Wow! We are really lucky to be part of Halima's flock." The flock finally reached the field where they would graze. The mother sheep, after having eaten her fill, lay down in the grass. The little lamb continued to ask his mother questions about the Child of Light. Everybody loved the child, just like the sheep did, and they always wanted to talk about him. The little lamb asked in his highpitched bleat: "Mommy, can you tell me about your life before the Child of Light came to the plateau?"

The mother looked off into the distance. "You have heard about our owner, Halima" she began. "In Mecca, the Child of Light came into this world; he was very wonderful. His grandfather gave him the name of Muhammad (peace and blessings be upon him) which means "the one who is praised."

His sweet mother's name was Amina, and his father's name was Abdullah, my dear. His father died before he was born. His mother and grandfather, Abdulmuttalib looked after him.

"Well, when did the Child of Light come to the plateau, Mommy?"

"Our beloved Muhammad came here when he was a baby."

12

From that day on Halima and her family have loved him very much and they have protected him. When the Child of Light was a baby you hadn't yet been born, my dear," his mother said.

The little lamb said: "I love it when he strokes me with his rose-scented hands."

His mother answered: "My dear, he is the most beautiful and best child in the whole world. Allah has given him qualities that other children don't have. He brings happiness wherever he goes.

14

He is well-mannered, honest, respectful and helpful."
After listening, the little lamb said to his mother:
"Thank God you were born, Child of Light! Wherever you are there is happiness; wherever you are there is plenty; wherever you are there is security. You are wonderful, Child of Light!"
The little lamb's mother then said that it was time they started home; the little lamb couldn't bear for a long time to pass without seeing the Child of Light.

The mother had eaten plenty, and they started to trot off home. With every step they took closer to the Child of Light, the little lamb became happier and happier.